PAPER FLIERS

Written by Alan Folder
Illustrated by Maureen Galvani
Photography by Stillview

Copyright © 2000 Top That! Publishing plc
Published by Tangerine Press™, an imprint of Scholastic Inc.
555 Broadway, New York, NY 10012.

All rights reserved
Scholastic and Tangerine Press™ and associated logos are trademarks of Scholastic Inc. No part of this work
may be reproduced, stored in a retrieval system, or transmitted in any form or by any means electronic,
mechanical, photocopying, recording or otherwise, without the prior permission of Tangerine Press™.
Requests for such permissions should be addressed to Tangerine Press, 1080 Greenwood Blvd., Lake Mary,
FL 32746 USA.

Contents

Printed Papers

Introduction

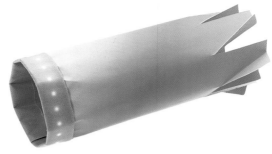

In this book, you'll discover lots of cool projects for you to create and fly, loop the loop, or set long-distance records. Also included are flying tips on how to keep your fabulous air force in the air.

Every flying project begins with a short list of materials you will need to get started. We have provided you with some beautifully designed, pre-printed sheets to create all the fliers in the book, which you'll find in the "Printed Papers" section. Each of the printed sheets has a number which corresponds to a particular project.

All you have to do is remove each sheet, cut the paper to the right size, if necessary, and you're ready to start folding! All you need is a pencil, ruler, scissors, glue, paper, and a few other everyday things you can find around the house. It is a good idea to keep all your materials in a safe place, like a box with a lid – out of reach of any younger family members. Scissors can be very sharp, so be careful not to cut yourself or damage any surfaces.

Remember, always be very careful NOT to hit anyone when throwing your airplanes.

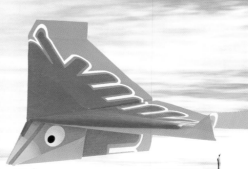

There's lots to keep you busy as you soar into the wild blue yonder with **PAPER FLIERS!**

3

Folding Tips

Before you start any of the projects in this book, here are some helpful tips that will make your folding easier:

- Before you start, make sure your paper is the right shape.

- Fold on a flat surface, like a table or a book.

- Make your folds and cuts neat and accurate.

- Crease your folds by running your thumbnail along them.

- Follow the instructions carefully.

Symbols & Basic Folding Procedures

The symbols in this book show the direction in which the paper should be folded. Before trying any of the projects, study the following diagrams to see which way the dots, dashes, and arrows go over, through, and under the paper.

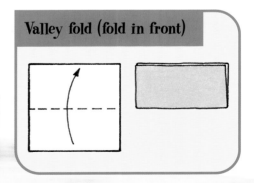

Valley fold (fold in front)

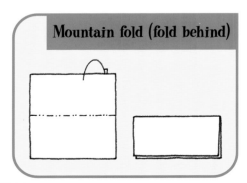

Mountain fold (fold behind)

Fold over and over

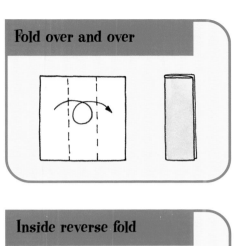

Outside reverse fold

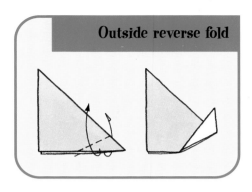

Inside reverse fold

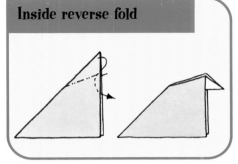

Fold and unfold

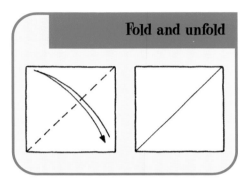

Turn paper over

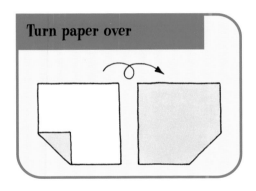

Cut

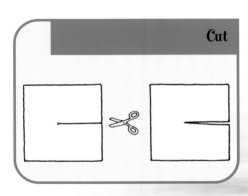

Rotate paper

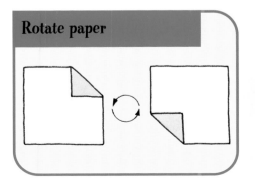

Insert

Open out

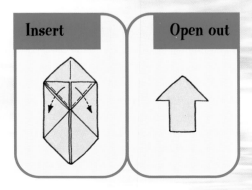

Flying Fish

You will need:
- A rectangle of paper.
- Scissors.

1 Using the first paper provided, place the rectangle sideways. Cut a long strip of paper about 0.78 in. (2 cm) wide. We have supplied eight strips.

0.78 in.
(2 cm)

2 On the strip's lower right-hand side, cut halfway across the strip. Repeat on the strip's upper left-hand side.

3 Bring one cut over to meet the other and…

4 …slip them into each other, so they are linked. This completes the Flying Fish.

HOW TO FLY:

Throw the Flying Fish high into the air, and watch it twist and turn on its way to the ground.

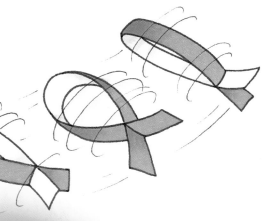

Helicopter

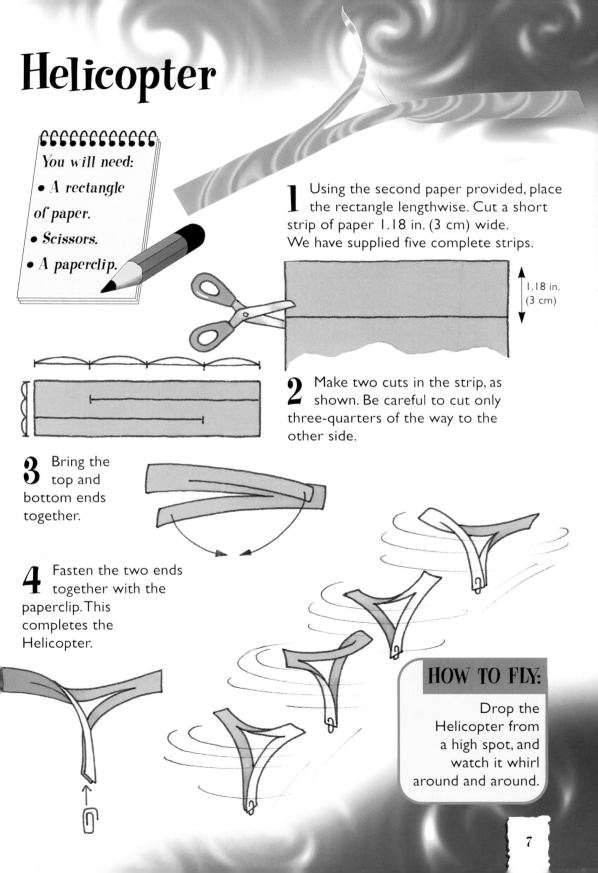

You will need:
- A rectangle of paper.
- Scissors.
- A paperclip.

1 Using the second paper provided, place the rectangle lengthwise. Cut a short strip of paper 1.18 in. (3 cm) wide. We have supplied five complete strips.

1.18 in. (3 cm)

2 Make two cuts in the strip, as shown. Be careful to cut only three-quarters of the way to the other side.

3 Bring the top and bottom ends together.

4 Fasten the two ends together with the paperclip. This completes the Helicopter.

HOW TO FLY:

Drop the Helicopter from a high spot, and watch it whirl around and around.

Tumbling Butterfly

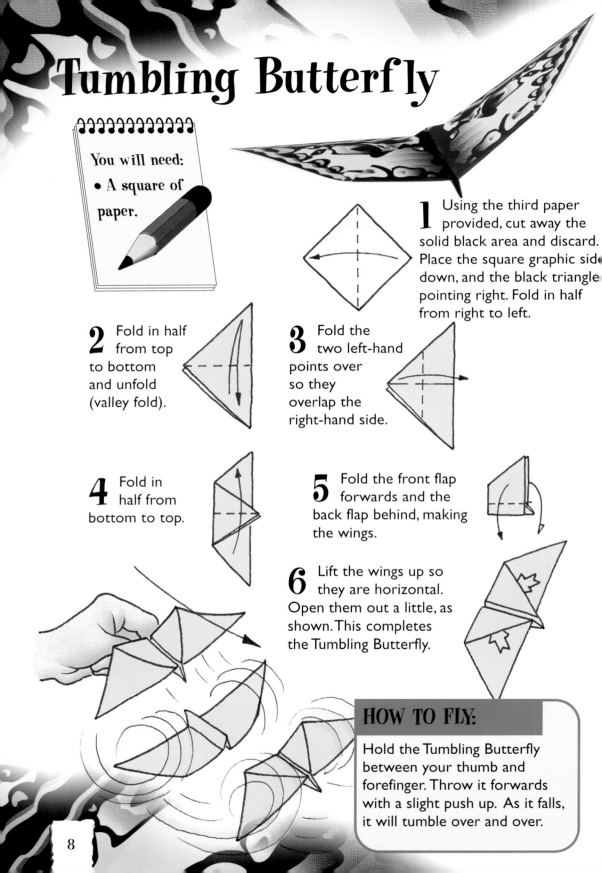

You will need:

• A square of paper.

1 Using the third paper provided, cut away the solid black area and discard. Place the square graphic side down, and the black triangle pointing right. Fold in half from right to left.

2 Fold in half from top to bottom and unfold (valley fold).

3 Fold the two left-hand points over so they overlap the right-hand side.

4 Fold in half from bottom to top.

5 Fold the front flap forwards and the back flap behind, making the wings.

6 Lift the wings up so they are horizontal. Open them out a little, as shown. This completes the Tumbling Butterfly.

HOW TO FLY:

Hold the Tumbling Butterfly between your thumb and forefinger. Throw it forwards with a slight push up. As it falls, it will tumble over and over.

Fighter Dart

1 Using the fourth paper provided, place on its side, white side up, stripes on the right. Fold in half from bottom to top and unfold.

You will need:
• A rectangle of paper.

2 Fold the left-hand corners over to meet the middle fold-line.

3 Fold the left-hand sloping edges over to meet the middle fold-line.

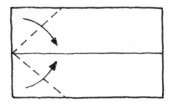

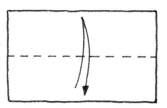

4 Fold in half, taking the paper behind from bottom to top (mountain fold).

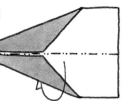

5 Fold the front flap down and…

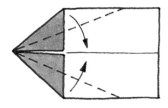

6 ..the back flap down, making the wings.

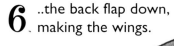

7 Lift the wings up so they are horizontal. This completes the Fighter Dart.

HOW TO FLY:

Hold the Dart between your thumb and forefinger. Throw it firmly at a slight upwards angle.

Circular Aerofoil

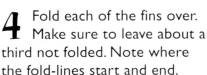

You will need:
- A rectangle of paper.
- Scissors.
- Tape or glue.

1 Using the fifth paper provided, place it on its side, rainbow effect facing up, and the purple color to the left. Fold in half from side to side and unfold.

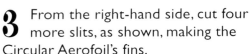

2 From the right-hand side, cut three slits in the paper, as shown.

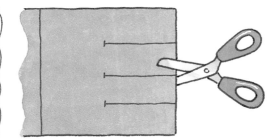

3 From the right-hand side, cut four more slits, as shown, making the Circular Aerofoil's fins.

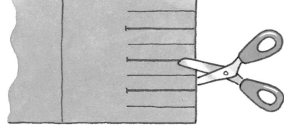

4 Fold each of the fins over. Make sure to leave about a third not folded. Note where the fold-lines start and end.

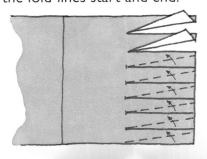

5 Fold the left-hand side over to meet the middle fold-line.

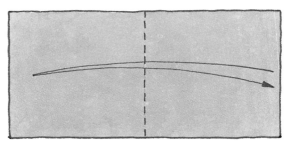

6 Again, fold the left-hand side over to meet the middle fold-line.

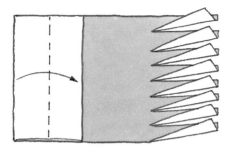

7 Fold the left-hand side over one more time to meet the middle fold-line.

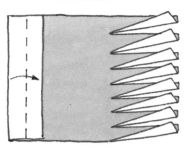

8 Turn the paper over. Bend the paper into a tube, so the top and bottom edges slightly overlap.

9 Hold the overlapping edges in place with tape or glue. Stand the fins up straight. This completes the Circular Aerofoil.

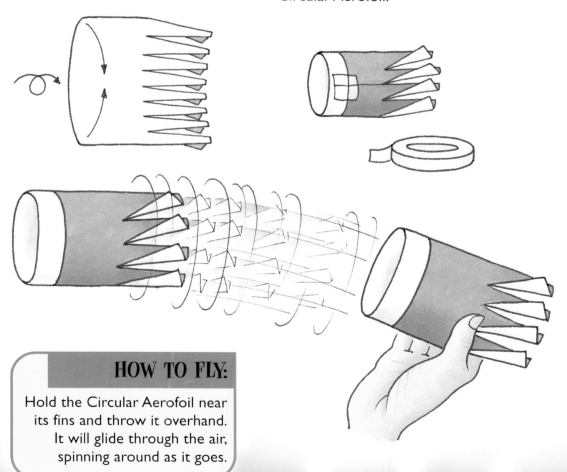

HOW TO FLY:

Hold the Circular Aerofoil near its fins and throw it overhand. It will glide through the air, spinning around as it goes.

Swallow Plane

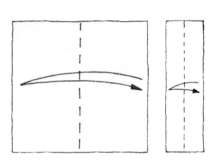

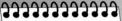

You will need:
• A square of paper. • A narrow rectangle for the tail.
• Scissors.

1 Using the sixth paper provided, cut along the yellow lines to remove the tail. Place the body square face down, feathers and eyes pointing down. Fold in half from side to side and unfold. Repeat with the tail.

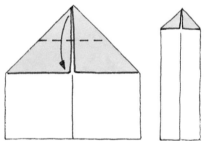

2 Fold the body's top corners down to meet the middle fold-line. Repeat with the tail strip, feathers down and nearest you.

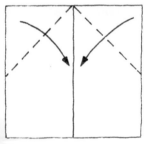

3 Fold the body's top point down, as shown.

4 Fold the body down along the middle fold-line.

5 Tuck the tail underneath the body, as shown.

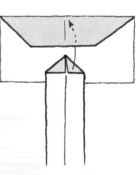

6 Fold the body's top corners down to meet the center fold-line, to make the wings.

7 Fold the paper behind in half, from side to side, so the design is showing.

8 Rotate the paper, as shown. Fold the front wing down forward and the back wing down behind. Cut off the right-hand point of the tail, as shown by the shading.

9 Lift the wings up so they are horizontal. This completes the Swallow Plane.

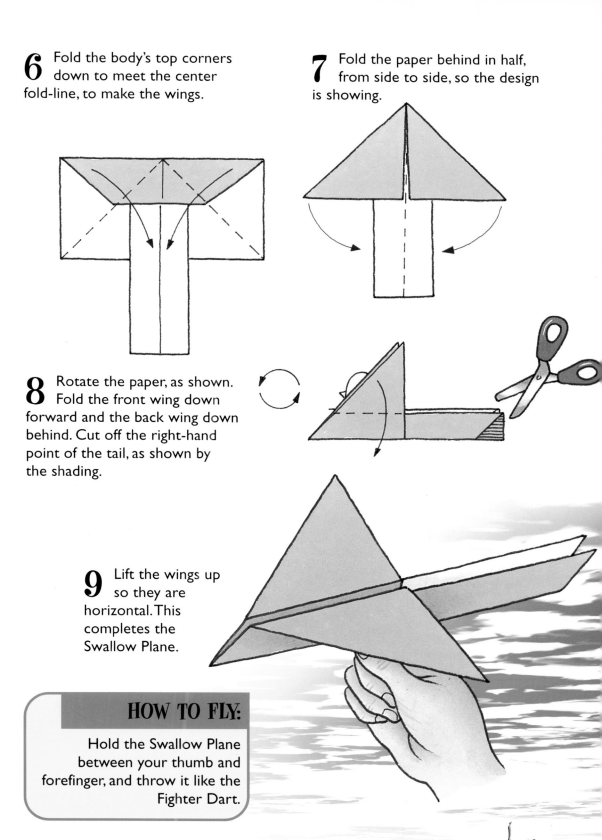

HOW TO FLY:

Hold the Swallow Plane between your thumb and forefinger, and throw it like the Fighter Dart.

Flying Propeller

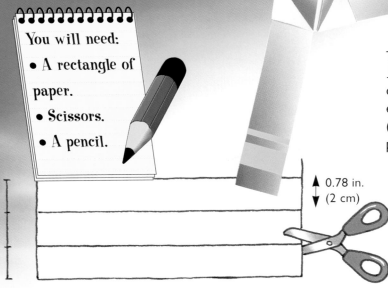

You will need:
- **A rectangle of paper.**
- **Scissors.**
- **A pencil.**

1 Using the seventh paper provided, cut three short strips, each about 0.78 in. (2 cm) wide – we have provided eight pieces.

↕ 0.78 in. (2 cm)

2 Place the strips color side down, with the red triangle to the left of center. Using the pencil, label the strips A, B, and C. Fold each strip in half from right to left.

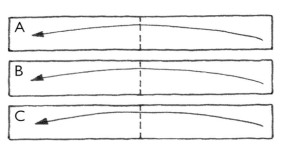

3 Take strips A and B, with the red triangles facing down, and put A inside B, as shown.

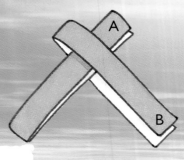

4 Weave strip C, also with the red triangle facing down, into place.

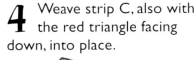

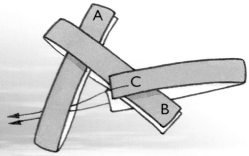

5 Pull the strips out and up in the directions shown.

A

C

B

6 Turn the strips over so the red triangles are facing upwards, and pull into a tight knot.

A

C

B

7 Fold each of the strips along the broken lines and unfold, as shown…

8 …making them stand out from the knot. This completes the Flying Propeller.

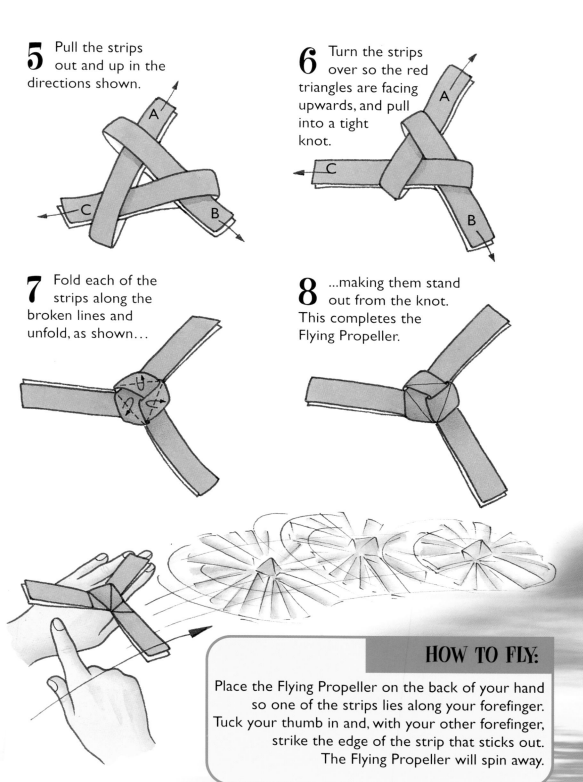

HOW TO FLY:

Place the Flying Propeller on the back of your hand so one of the strips lies along your forefinger. Tuck your thumb in and, with your other forefinger, strike the edge of the strip that sticks out. The Flying Propeller will spin away.

Gliding Ring

You will need:
- A square of paper.
- Tape.

1 Using the eighth paper provided, cut away the solid orange area and discard. Place the graphic side down, and the black at the top and bottom. Fold in half from bottom to top.

2 Fold the bottom edge up...

3 ...making a small strip of paper. Turn the paper over.

4 Bring the ends of the strip up and over to meet and...

5 ...slide one into the other, making a ring-like shape. Tape in place. Curve the ring to make it as circular as possible. This completes the Gliding Ring.

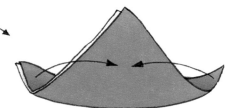

HOW TO FLY:

Hold the Gliding Ring, as shown. Throw with a gentle push forwards, and watch it glide through the air, slowly landing.

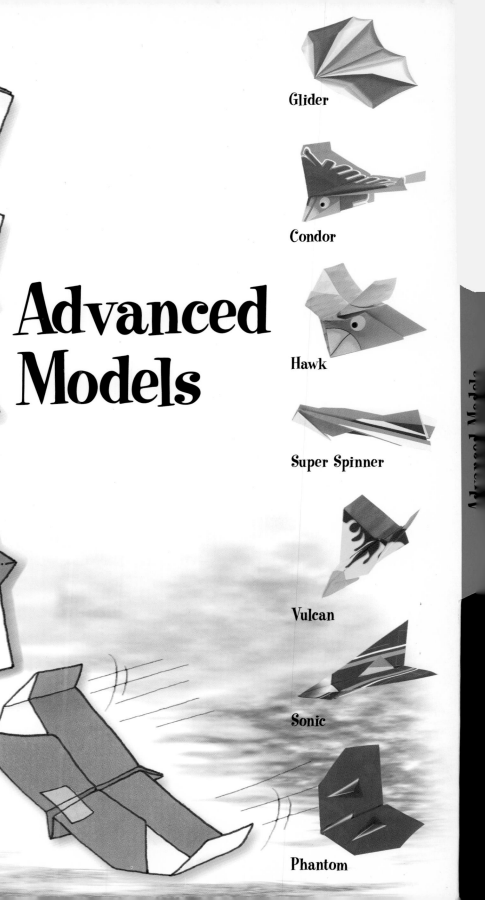

Advanced Models

Glider

Condor

Hawk

Super Spinner

Vulcan

Sonic

Phantom

Introduction to the Advanced Section

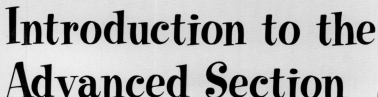

Now that you have mastered the basic projects, it is time to try out some of the more difficult projects featured in the following pages.

When you have used up all the printed paper in this book, you can use plain or brown paper, and decorate the models yourself. Try using stickers and markers to jazz up the planes, or try glitter, stars, and sequins. If you're really on a tight budget, try using old posters or leftover wallpaper. Gift wrap from stationery stores, old newspapers, and magazine pages are good alternatives. Whatever you use, you can make your planes look fantastic without spending all your pocket money.

When you have made your planes, you can have a competition with your friends to see whose flies the best!

Glider

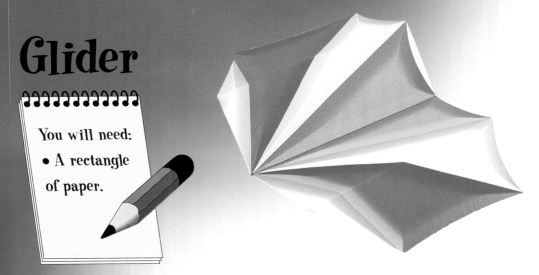

You will need:
• A rectangle of paper.

1 Using the ninth paper provided, place it lengthways with the graphic side down. Fold in half from side to side and unfold.

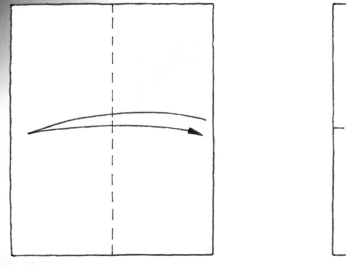

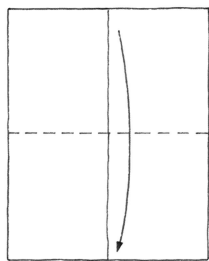

2 Fold in half from top to bottom.

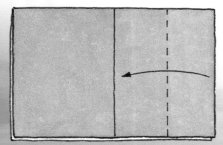

3 Fold the right-hand edge over to meet the middle fold-line.

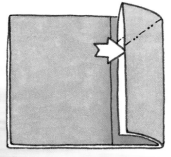

4 Lift the side up and open its layers of paper out.

5 Press the top down into the shape of a triangle. Repeat steps 3 to 5 with the left-hand side.

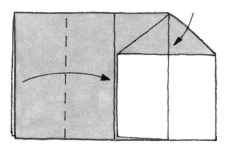

6 Fold the center pane behind, but on top of the bottom paper, and meet the triangles' bottom edges.

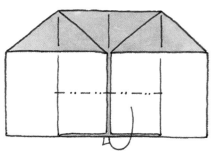

7 Fold the center panel again, tucking it underneath the triangles.

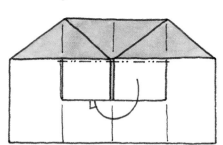

8 Fold the left-hand side behind to meet the right-hand side.

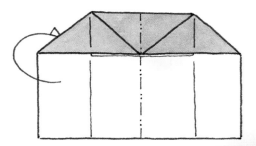

9 Rotate the paper, as shown. Fold the front flap down forwards, and the back flap down behind, making the wings.

10 Lift the wings up so they are horizontal. This completes the Glider.

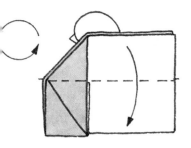

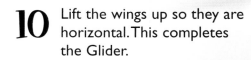

HOW TO FLY:

Hold the Glider between your thumb and forefinger and throw it like the Fighter Dart.

Condor

You will need:
• A rectangle of paper.

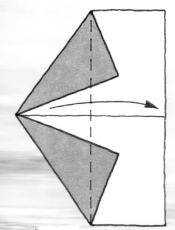

1 Using the tenth paper provided, place lengthwise, face down with the beak to the left. Fold the opposite edges together in turn, press flat, and open up.

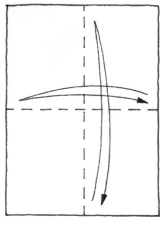

2 Fold the left-hand corners over. The corners do not meet the middle fold line, as shown in step three.

3 Fold the left-hand point over to meet the middle of the opposite side, as shown.

4 Again, fold the left-hand corners over.

5 Fold the sloping edges under, as shown.

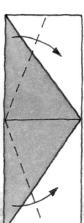

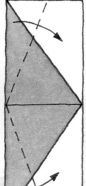

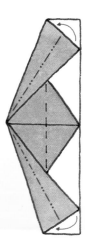

6 Fold the right-hand triangle over to the left, as shown.

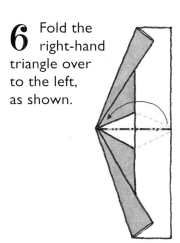

7 Fold the plane in half with the top and bottom edges touching.

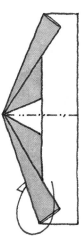

8 Fold the front flap down forward, and the back flap down behind, making the wings.

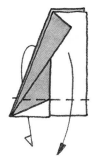

9 Fold half of the wing up. Repeat on the other wing.

10 Fold a little of the wing's top edge behind. Repeat with the back wing.

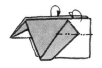

11 Open up the wings, as shown. This completes the Condor.

HOW TO FLY:

Gently throw high into the air and watch the Condor float gracefully downwards.

Hawk

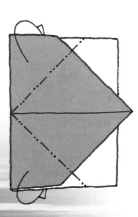

You will need:
- A rectangle of paper.
- Tape.

1 Using the eleventh paper provided, place sideways with the graphic side down, and the feathers to the right. Fold in half from bottom to top and unfold.

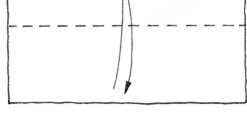

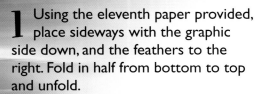

2 Fold the left-hand corners over to meet the middle fold-line.

3 Fold the left-hand point over, so it overlaps the right-hand side with the eyes and beak visible.

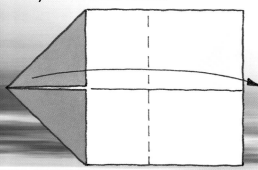

4 Fold the left-hand corners behind to meet the middle fold-line.

5 Fold the left-hand point over to the right, so the beak and eyes are visible.

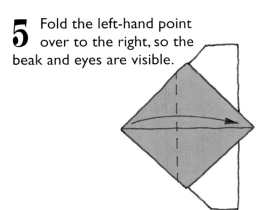

6 Fold the bottom edge behind and up to the top edge.

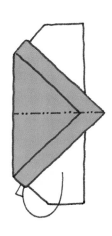

7 Fold the front flap down forward, and the back flap down behind, making the wings.

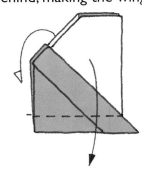

8 Fold over a little of the front wing's bottom edge up. Repeat on the other wing.

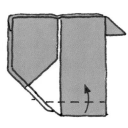

9 Open up the wings, as shown. Hold the wings together with a piece of tape. This completes the Hawk.

HOW TO FLY:

Hold the Hawk between your thumb and forefinger, and throw it like the Fighter Dart.

Super Spinner

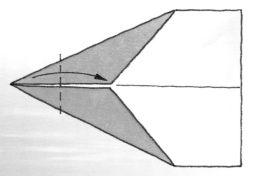

You will need:
- A rectangle of paper.
- Tape.

1 Using the twelfth paper provided, place it on its side, with the red graphic side down, and the triangles to the right. Fold in half from bottom to top and unfold.

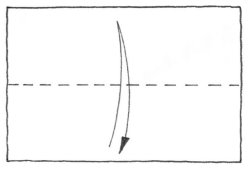

2 Fold the left-hand corners over to meet the middle fold-line.

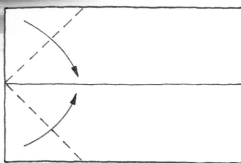

3 Fold the left-hand sloping edges over to meet the middle fold-line.

4 Fold the left-hand point over, as shown.

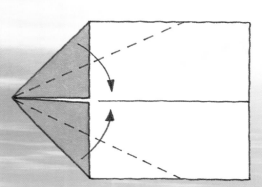

5 Fold the bottom edge behind to the top edge.

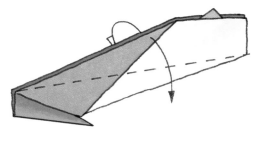

6 Push the lower right-hand corner up and inside the model, as shown, making the tail.

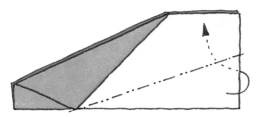
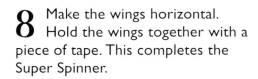

7 Fold the front flap down and the back flap down on the other side, making the wings.

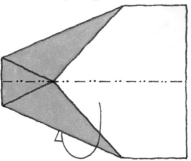

8 Make the wings horizontal. Hold the wings together with a piece of tape. This completes the Super Spinner.

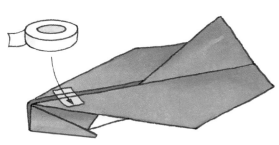

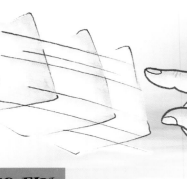

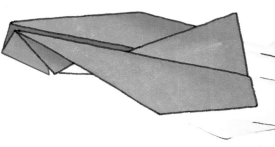

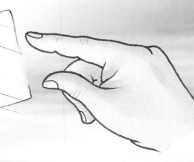

HOW TO FLY:

Hold the Super Spinner between your thumb and forefinger, and throw it like the Condor.

Vulcan

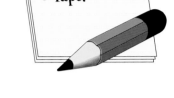

You will need:
- A rectangle of paper.
- Tape.

1 Using the thirteenth paper provided, place it on its side, with the flames down, and facing right. Fold in half from bottom to top and unfold.

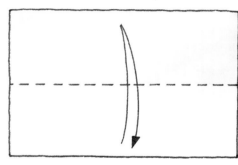

2 Fold the left-hand corners over to meet the middle fold-line.

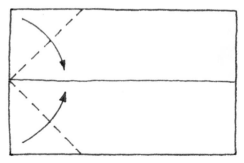

4 Fold the left-hand side over one-fifth of the way to the right, where the red print area meets the black on the paper.

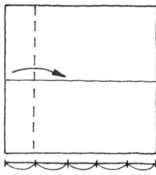

3 Fold the left-hand point behind, as shown.

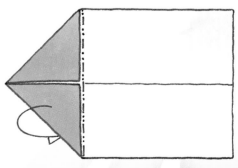

5 Again, fold the left-hand corners over to meet the middle fold-line.

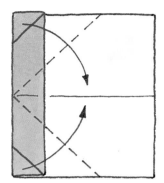

6 Fold the plane in half from bottom to top.

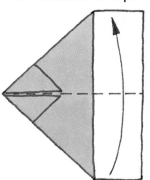

7 Fold the front flap down at an angle. Repeat on the other flap.

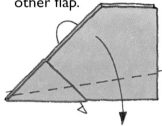

8 Fold the front flap up at an angle, and repeat with the back flap, making the wings, as shown.

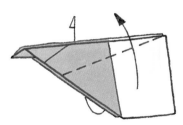

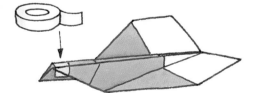

9 Open up the wings, as shown. Hold the folds together with a piece of tape. This completes the Vulcan.

HOW TO FLY:

Hold the Vulcan between your thumb and forefinger, and throw it like the Fighter Dart.

Sonic

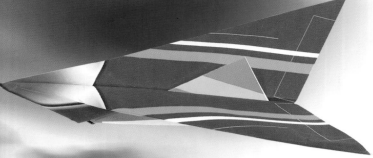

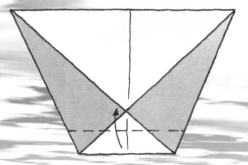

ooooooooooo

You will need:

• A rectangle
of paper.

• Tape.

1 Using the fourteenth paper provided, place it on its side, with the green side down, and the blue triangle on top, pointing down. Fold in half from side to side and unfold.

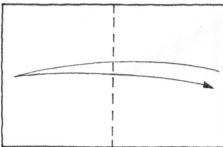

2 Fold the bottom corners over diagonally so the points meet the middle fold-line.

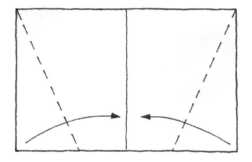

3 Fold the bottom edge up as far as shown.

4 Fold the bottom edge over.

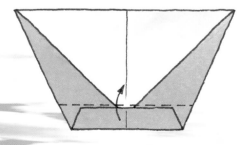

5 Fold the sides over diagonally to meet the adjacent edges.

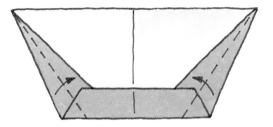

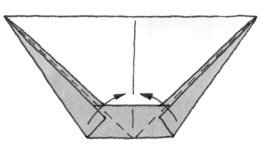

6 Fold the sides over so the bottoms meet on the middle fold-line.

7 Fold in half so the points meet on the backside.

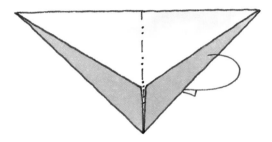

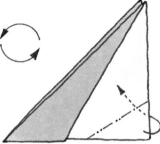

8 Rotate the paper, as shown. Push the lower right-hand corner up, and inside the model, as shown, making the tail.

9 Fold the front flap down, and repeat with the back flap, making the wings.

10 Open up the wings. Hold the folds together with a piece of tape. This completes the Sonic.

HOW TO FLY:

Hold the Sonic between your thumb and forefinger, and throw it like the Condor.

Phantom

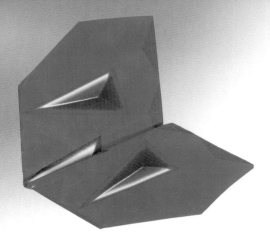

You will need:
- A rectangle of paper.
- Tape.

1 Using the fifteenth paper provided, place it on its side, with the graphic side down, and triangles to the right. Fold in half from bottom to top and unfold.

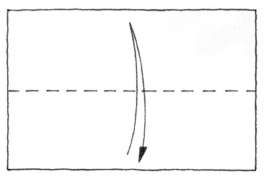

2 Fold the left-hand corners over to meet the middle fold-line.

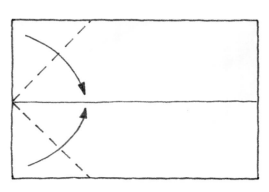

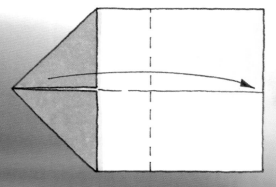

3 Fold the left-hand point over to meet the middle of the opposite edge.

4 Again, fold the left-hand corners over to meet the middle fold-line.

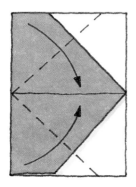

5 Fold the small right-hand triangle over towards the left.

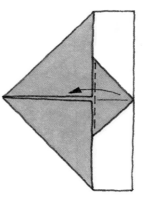

6 Fold the left-hand point over towards the right and...

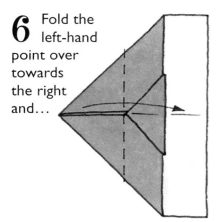

7 ... tuck it inside the plane.

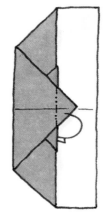

8 Fold the bottom edge behind to the top edge.

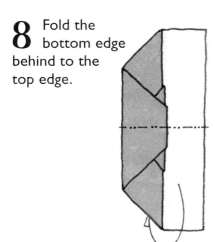

9 Push the lower right-hand corner up and inside the model to create the tail.

10 Fold the front flap down and repeat with the back flap, making the wings.

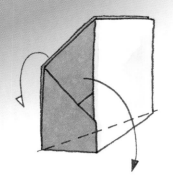

11 Open up the wings, as shown. Hold the folds together with a piece of tape. This completes the Phantom.

HOW TO FLY:

Hold the Phantom between your thumb and forefinger, and throw it like the Condor.

Printed Papers

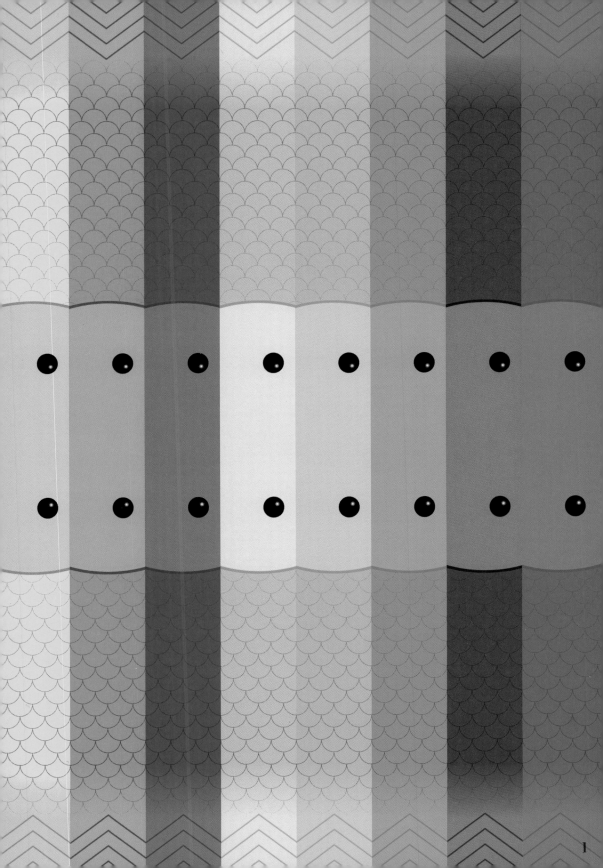

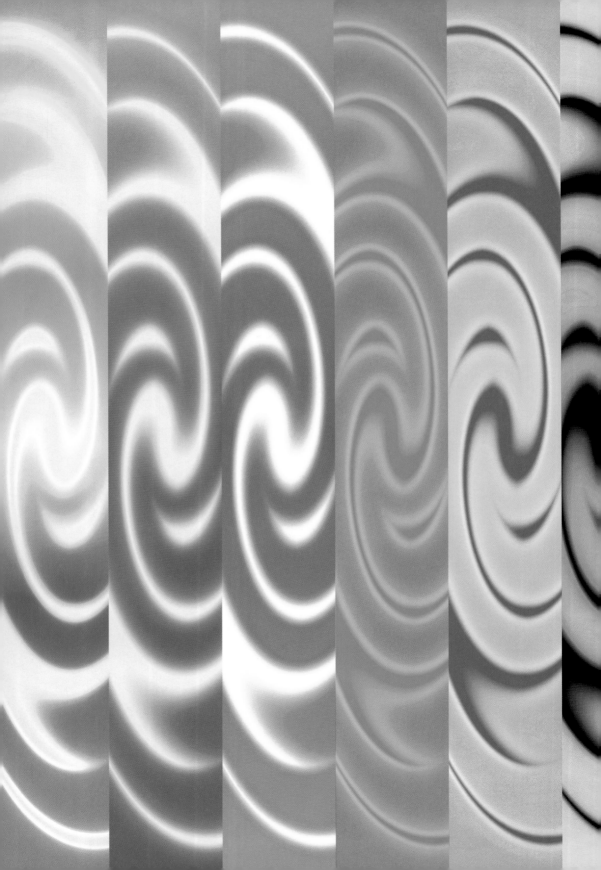

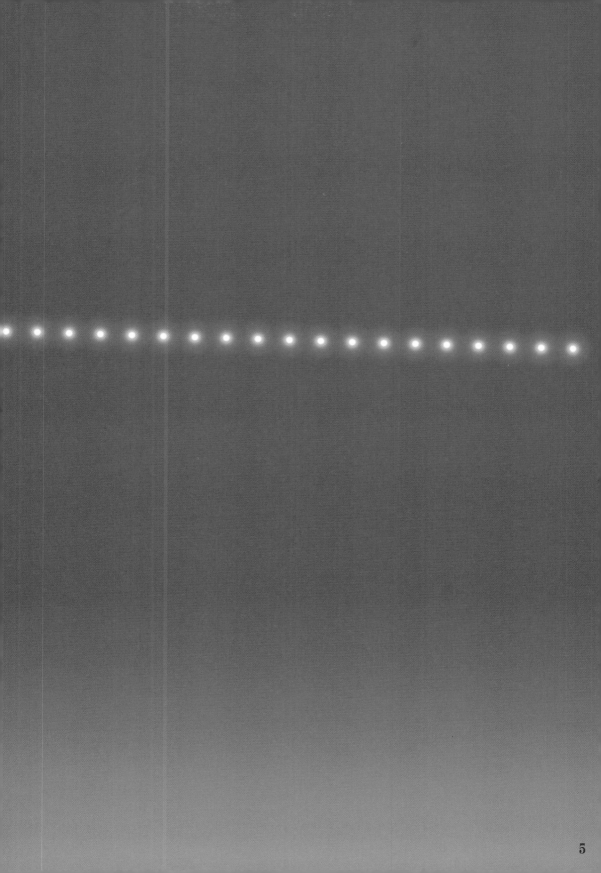

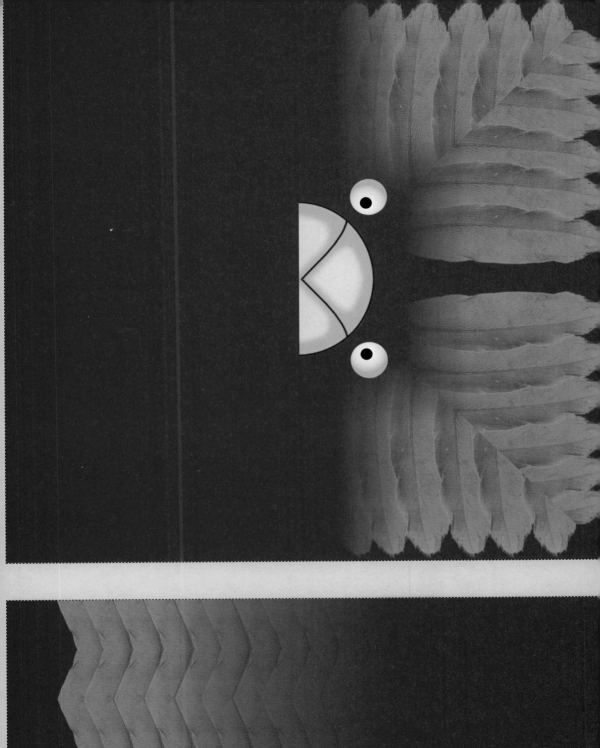

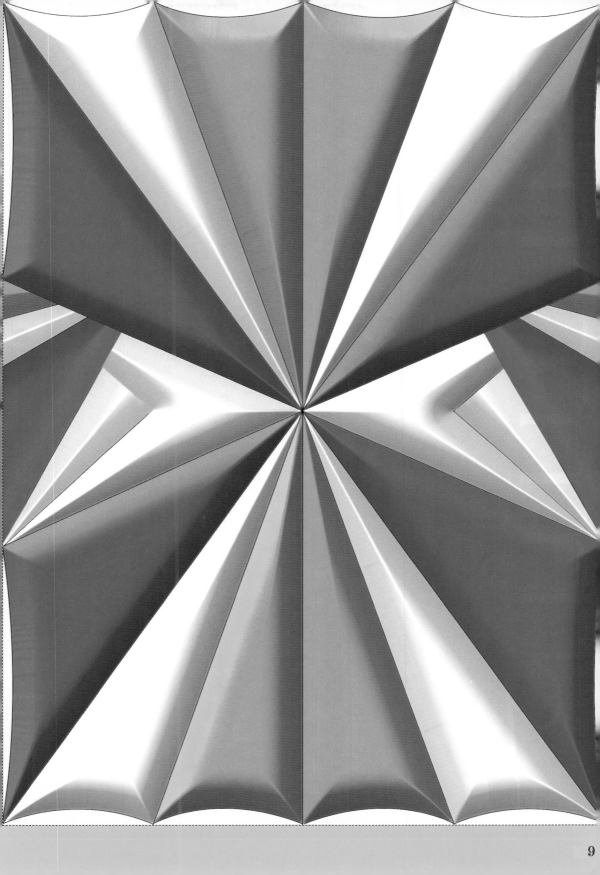

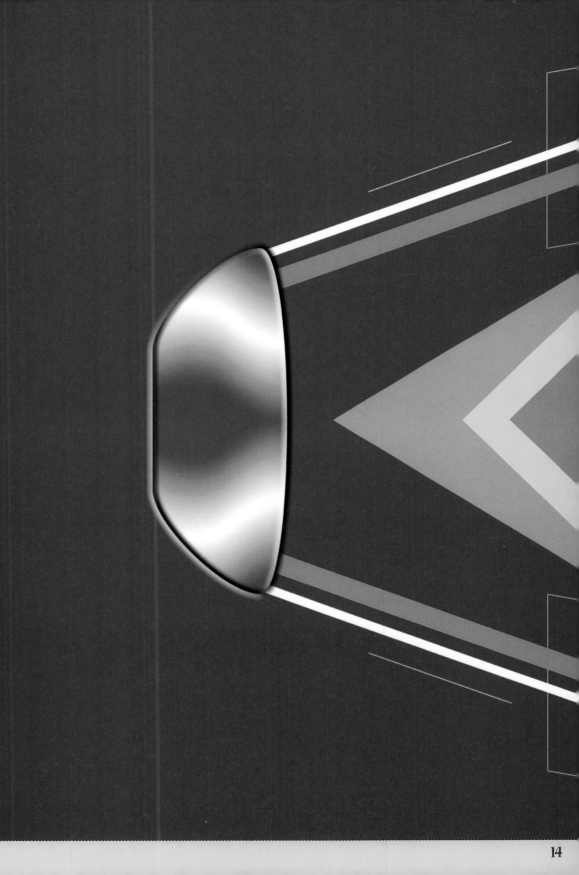